Clarinet part

the best of grade 4
Clarinet

A compilation of the best Grade 4 clarinet pieces ever selected by the major examination boards

Selected and edited by Paul Harris

Audio tracks are available by scanning the QR code or from fabermusic.com/audio.

© 2010 by Faber Music Ltd
This edition first published in 2010
Bloomsbury House
74–77 Great Russell Street
London WC1B 3DA
Music processed by Jackie Leigh
Design by Økvik Design
Printed in England by Caligraving Ltd
All rights reserved

ISBN10: 0-571-53424-4
EAN13: 978-0-571-53424-1

To buy Faber Music publications or to find out about the full range of titles available
please contact your local music retailer or Faber Music sales enquiries:

Faber Music Limited, Burnt Mill, Elizabeth Way, Harlow CM20 2HX
Tel: +44 (0)1279 82 89 82
fabermusic.com

All audio tracks recorded in London, February 2010
Performed by Charlotte Swift (Clarinet) and Robin Bigwood (Piano)

Engineered by Robin Bigwood; Produced by Fiona Bolton
℗ 2010 Faber Music Ltd © 2010 Faber Music Ltd

Contents

The performers

Charlotte Swift studied at Cambridge University and the Royal Academy of Music. She has won many competitions, was principal clarinet in the National Youth Orchestra for many years, and is now establishing a thriving career as a soloist, orchestral and chamber music player.

Robin Bigwood is a freelance pianist and harpsichordist, performing with Passacaglia, Feinstein Ensemble, Britten Sinfonia and as a soloist. He also works as a sound engineer and producer.

Track 1: Tuning note B flat

Rondeau

from 'First Book of Clarinet Solos'

The baroque rondeau was a gentle dance. Play this piece with a graceful lilt and your best singing tone. The dynamic contrasts need not be too exaggerated.

Henry Purcell (1659–1695)
arr. Alan Richardson

Theme from Variations on a Rococo Theme

from 'Going Solo'

PERFORMANCE ④
ACCOMPANIMENT ⑤

Give this the feel of an elegant courtly dance. *Staccato* notes should be light but not too short. Don't breathe in the semiquaver rests (in bars 6 and 14); after the following note would be better.

Pyotr Ilyich Tchaikovsky (1840–1893)
arr. Paul Harris

Allegretto from Concertpiece No.3 in B♭

from 'Clarinet Basics Repertoire'

Prior to practising the piece, play C major scale and arpeggio evenly, at various speeds and at the various dynamic markings used in this piece. Keep your fingers close to the tone holes so they can be nimble.

Franz Danzi (1763–1826)
arr. Paul Harris

To be played with repeat

Sicilienne

from 'Going Solo'

This beautiful melody must flow along with a smooth and warm tone quality. Listen out for unwanted bumps or accents. Don't breathe after the D in bar 20 as this would spoil the climax.

Maria Theresia Paradis (1759–1824)

arr. Paul Harris

Schlummerlied

from 'Second Book of Clarinet Solos'

The title means slumber song or lullaby so the tone needs to be flowing and gentle. A little subtle flexibility in the tempo now and then would add to the style and character.

Carl Baermann (1810–1885)

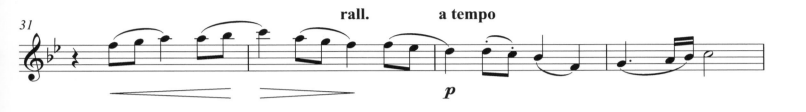

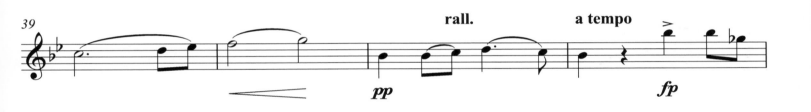

Gymnopédie No.1

from 'Clarinet Basics Repertoire'

PERFORMANCE 12
ACCOMPANIMENT 13

The first note in each phrase needs a delicate and rounded attack. Sustain the long notes with a well-controlled and constant *diminuendo*. Practise *really* long notes in preparation!

Erik Satie (1866–1925)
arr. Paul Harris

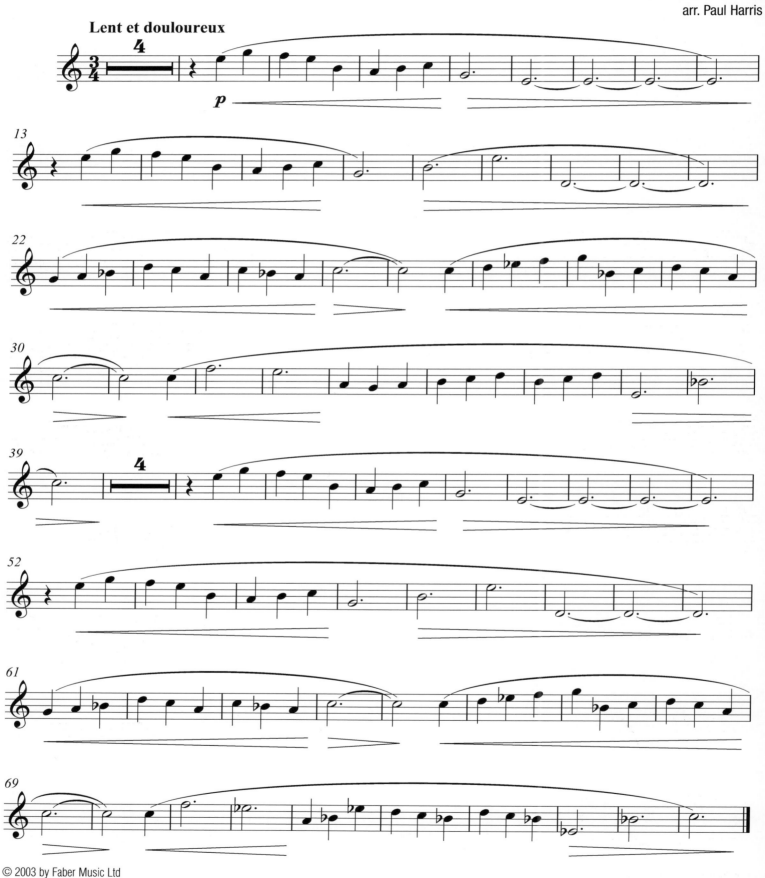

Stick Together

from 'Microjazz Clarinet Collection 2'

PERFORMANCE [14]
ACCOMPANIMENT [15]

Lots of off-beat accents (lively, but not too heavy) will add to the jazzy character. Try playing the grace notes on the beat and don't shorten the long notes (e.g. the tied D in bar 1).

Christopher Norton

Estuary

from 'Going Solo'

Give this melody a sense of floating by thinking in four-bar phrases. Aim for you best *legato* and try to cross the break as smoothly as possible.

Christopher Gunning

Pastoral

from 'Four Short Pieces'

Aim for a very expressive and thoughtful character and a warm and rich tone quality. Work carefully at the changes of tempo in bar 21 and 38. The grace notes should be played gently.

Howard Ferguson (1908–1999)

To John Newberry

Taurus

from 'The Zodiac Set 1'

Enjoy the energy and fun of this colourful piece. Make your *forte* strong but not too bright, and be careful not to rush the semiquavers. The contrasted section from bar 19 to 26 can be much more lyrical.

Brian Kelly

Study No.44 – The Turn

from '80 Graded Studies for Clarinet Book One'

The *turn* is a particular kind of melodic decoration. Use the pattern given below and don't rush the notes. Try to maintain a pure and focussed tone in this charming melody and add more dynamic markings of your own.

PERFORMANCE 22

Henry Lazarus (1815–1895)

Sevenths in Swing

from 'Times Ten'

Swing the quavers gently and lift the fourth note in each grouping lightly to create a jazzy flavour. Use the contrasting dynamics to bring the piece to life.

Jeffery Wilson

Study in C

from 'Methode Complete de Clarinette'

This is a good study to improve your tonguing. Always maintain the airflow to ensure good tone quality and keep the tongue action light.

Moderato

Frédéric Berr (1794–1838)

Prelude from L'Arlésienne

PERFORMANCE

from 'Woodwind World Book 4'

There is lots to think about in this study — dotted rhythms, tonguing, *legato*, grace notes and
contrasted dynamic levels. It's a great tune too; try to listen to the original orchestral version.

Georges Bizet (1838–1875)

Study in G

from 'Clarinet School'

PERFORMANCE 26

Aim for flowing *legato* lines with no bumps as you cross the break and only gentle emphasis on the accented notes. Sub-divide bar 8 into semiquavers to secure the rhythm.

Hyacinthe Klosé (1808–1895)

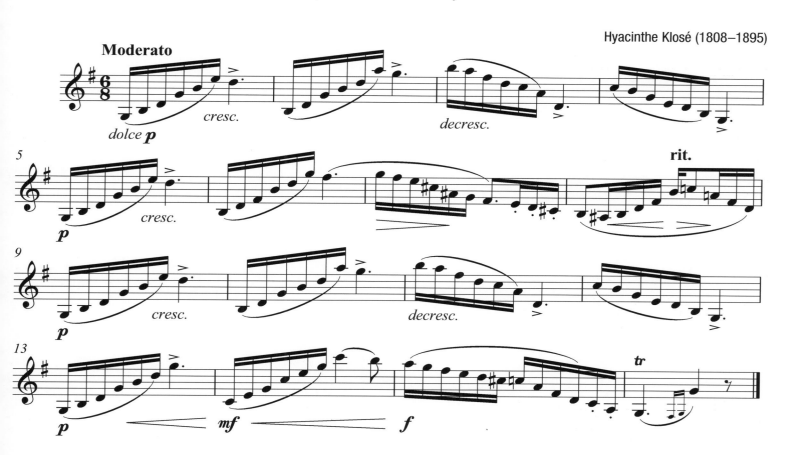